MONEY MATH

BY DONN MOSENFELDER

Caleb E. Crowell, Editorial Director

ISBN# 0-87694-216-8   EDI 381

TABLE OF CONTENTS

SECTION D

SECTION A

1 COINS

(25¢) a quarter = 25¢ = $.25

(10¢) a dime = 10¢ = $.10

(5¢) a nickel = 5¢ = $.05   (Note the 0 in front of the 5.)

(1¢) a penny = 1¢ = $.01   (Note the 0.)

(1¢)(1¢) 2 pennies = 2¢ = $.02   (From 1¢ to 9¢, write your decimal, then 0, then the number.)

Exercises

Circle your answers.

1. Four cents =

  a. $4
  b. $.04

2. Twenty cents =

  a. $20
  b. $.20

3. Thirty cents =

  a. $.30
  b. $.03

4. 3¢ =

  a. $.30
  b. $.03

5. 95¢ =

  a. $95
  b. $.95

6. 80¢ =

  a. $.80
  b. $80
  c. $.08

7. $.40 =

  a. 4 cents
  b. 40 cents
  c. 40 dollars

8. $.07 =

  a. 7 cents
  b. .7 cents
  c. .07 cents

9. $.02 =

  a. 2 pennies
  b. 2 nickels
  c. 2 dimes

10. $.20 =

  a. 2 pennies
  b. 2 nickels
  c. 2 dimes

2 COINS—PART II

$$\$.25 = 25\cancel{c} = \text{a quarter}$$
$$\$.10 = 10\cancel{c} = \text{a dime}$$
$$\$.05 = 5\cancel{c} = \text{a nickel}$$
$$\$.01 = 1\cancel{c} = \text{a penny}$$
$$\$.02 = 2\cancel{c} = 2 \text{ pennies}$$

Exercises

Write in your answers.

1. $.50 =

_____ (How many?)
quarters

2. $.10 =

_____ (How many?) dimes

3. $.10 =

_____ (How many?)
nickels

4. $.10 =

_____ (How many?)
pennies

5. Three cents =

$_____ (Be sure to put in
the decimal and the 0.)

6. 30¢ =

$_____ (Be sure to put in
the decimal.)

7. 11 pennies =

$_____ (Be sure to put in
the decimal.)

8. 6 pennies =

$_____ (Be sure to put in
the decimal and the 0.)

9. 9¢ =

$_____

10. 19 pennies =

$_____

3 COUNTING SMALL CHANGE

To count change, start with the biggest coins. Then add the next biggest. And so on. Try to do it out loud or in your head.

25 cents
(+ 25 cents) = 50 cents
(+ 10 cents) = 60 cents
(+ 5 cents) = 65 cents
(the final answer)

Exercises

See if you can add these in your head. If not, write down the numbers and add.

1. 25¢ 5¢ 1¢ = _____ (How many?) cents

2. 10¢ 10¢ 5¢ = _____ (How many?) cents

3.

= _____ (How many?) cents

4.

= _____ (How many?) cents

5.

= _____ (How many?) cents

6.
= _____ (How many?) cents

7.

= _____ (How many?) cents

8.
= _____ (How many?) cents

9.
= _____ (How many?) cents

10.

= _____ (How many?) cents

9

4 ▌▌▌▌▌▌▌▌▌▌▌▌▌▌▌▌▌▌▌▌▌▌▌▌▌▌▌▌▌▌▌▌▌▌▌
MAKING CHANGE

To make change, start with the amount owed. Then use your coins to "build."

Try to do it in your head.

You owe 37¢. You give the clerk 50¢.

She gives you 3¢ (to "build" the 37¢ to 40¢) and then a dime (to "build" from 40¢ to 50¢).

A friend owes you $.60. He gives you $1.

You give him a nickel (to "build" to $.65). Then a dime (to "build" from $.65 to $.75). Now you can use a quarter to "build" to a dollar.

▌▌▌ Exercises ◆

1. You owe 40¢. You give the clerk 50¢.

   a. How many nickels build to 50¢? _____
(Write the number.)

   b. How many dimes build from 40¢ to 50¢?

   _____

2. You owe 40¢. You give the clerk $1.

   a. How many dimes build to 50¢? _____

   b. How many quarters build from 50¢ to $1? _____

(Notice that you start with smaller coins to build to the nearest $.25, or $.50, or $.75. Then you can use quarters.)

3. You owe $.73. You give the clerk $1. She gives you:

   _____ (How many?) pennies (to build to $.75)

   _____ (How many?) quarters (to build from $.75 to $1.)

4. The customer owes $.79. She gives you $1. What change do you give her?

   _____ pennie(s)

   _____ dime(s)

5. The customer owes $1.65. He gives you $2. What change do you give him?

_____ nickel(s)

_____ quarter(s)

6. The customer owes $3.55. She gives you $4. What change do you give her?

_____ dime(s) (to build to $3.75)

_____ quarter(s) (to build to $4)

7. You owe 69¢. You give the clerk $1. What change does he give you?

_____

(What coin?) to build to 70¢

_____

(What coin?) to build to 75¢

_____

to build to $1

8. The customer owes $4.25. She gives you $5. What change do you give her?

_____ _____ (Note you only

(number)   (type of coin)   have to use one

type of coin.)

9. The customer owes $1.39. He gives you $1.50. What change do you give him?

number   coin

_____ _____ (to build to $1.40)

_____ _____ (to build to $1.50)

10. The customer owes $4.17. He gives you $5. What change do you give him?

number   coin

_____ _____

_____ _____

_____ _____

5 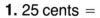 REVIEW

1. 25 cents =

  a. $25
  b. $.25
  c. $.025

2. 9 cents =

  a. $9
  b. $.90
  c. $.09

3. $.03 =

  a. 3 cents
  b. 30 cents
  c. 30 dollars

4. $.06 =

  a. 6 cents
  b. .6 cents
  c. .06 cents

5. $.30 =

  a. 3 dollars
  b. 3 dimes
  c. 3 pennies

6. $.04 =

  a. 4 dollars
  b. 4 dimes
  c. 4 pennies

7. $.30 =

  _____ (How many?) dimes

8. 5 cents =

  $_____ (Be sure to put
  in the decimal and 0.)

9. 12 cents =

  $_____

10. $.50 =

  2 _____ (What coin?)

11. $.15 =

  3 _____

12.

= _____ (How many?) cents

13.

= _____ (How many?) cents

12

14.

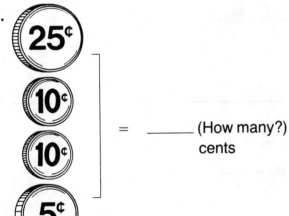 = _____ (How many?)
cents

15.

 = _____ (How many?)
cents

16. You owe $1.60. You give the clerk $2.
What change does she give you?

_____ nickel(s)

_____ quarter(s)

17. The customer owes $1.09. She gives you
a dollar and a quarter ($1.25). What change
do you give her?

number   coin

_____ _____

_____ _____

18. The customer owes $9.25. He gives you
$10. What change do you give him?

number   coin

_____ _____

19. The customer owes 38¢. He gives you $1.
What change do you give him?

number   coin

_____ _____

_____ _____

_____ _____

20. You owe $5.20. You give the clerk $6.
What change does he give you?

number   coin

_____ _____

_____ _____

6 DOLLARS

$$\$7 = \text{seven dollars}$$
$$\$13 = \text{thirteen dollars}$$
$$\$90 = \text{ninety dollars}$$
$$\$98 = \text{ninety-eight dollars}$$

You write the dollar amounts the same way you say them.

Exercises

1. $17 = _____ dollars (Spell it out.)

2. fifty-eight dollars = $_____

3. $24 = _____ – _____ dollars (Spell it out.)

4. seventy-nine dollars = $_____

5. $12 = _____ dollars

6. thirty-seven dollars = $_____

7. $57 = _____ – _____ dollars

8. forty-three dollars = _____ (Be sure to put in the dollar sign.)

9. $78 = _____ – _____

_____ (Be sure to write in "dollars.")

10. sixty-six dollars = _____ (Dollar sign!)

11. $30 = _____ _____

12. eighty dollars = _____

13. $19 = _____ _____

14. ninety-three dollars = _____

15. $75 = _____ — _____

_____

7 DOLLARS—PART II

$$\$700 = \text{seven hundred dollars}$$

$$\$7,000 = \text{seven thousand dollars}$$
(Watch the commas! The number in front of the comma tells you how many thousands.)

$$\$145 = \text{one hundred forty-five dollars}$$

$$\$2,145 = \text{two thousand one hundred forty-five dollars}$$

$$\$13,145 = \text{thirteen thousand one hundred forty-five dollars}$$

$$\$208,145 = \text{two hundred eight thousand one hundred forty-five dollars}$$

Exercises

1. Match. (Draw lines to connect the right answers. We have done this first problem for you.)

$30,000   three thousand dollars
$3,000   thirty thousand dollars

2. Match.

$10,000   ten thousand dollars
$100,000   one hundred thousand dollars

3. Match.

$5,100   fifty-one thousand dollars
$51,000   five thousand one hundred dollars

4. Match.

$988   nine hundred eighty-eight dollars
$98,800   ninety-eight thousand eight hundred dollars

5. Match.

$16,100   sixteen thousand one hundred dollars

$1,610   one thousand six hundred ten dollars

6. Put the comma in the right place.

$6000

7. Put the comma in the right place.

$60000

8. Put the comma in the right place.

$600000

9. Put the comma in the right place.

$2845

10. Put the comma in the right place.

$49029

11. thirty-nine thousand dollars = _____
(Be sure to put in the $ sign and comma.)

12. seven thousand, two hundred dollars = _____
(Don't forget the dollar sign and comma!)

13. seventeen thousand, two hundred dollars = _____

14. forty-nine thousand, eight hundred three dollars = _____

15. six hundred thirteen thousand dollars = _____

16. $4,000 = _____ (Spell it out.)

17. $4,205 = _____

18. $50,000 = _____

19. $500,000 = _____

20. $775,300 = _____

8 WHICH IS BIGGER?

Which is bigger?

$**5**79

$**5**89

Start at left, next to $ signs. **5** is the same in both numbers.

Go to next number. 8 is bigger than 7. $5**8**9 is bigger than $5**7**9.

Which is bigger?

$37,213

$37,095

In both numbers, 37 is the same. But 2 (next number) is bigger than 0. $37,213 is bigger than $37,095.

Exercises

1. Which is bigger? (Circle your answer.)

$5,529

$5,929

2. Which is bigger?

$19,035

$19,105

3. Which is bigger?

$493,888

$491,953

4. Which is bigger?

$800,311

$803,011

5. Which is bigger?

$5,055

$5,005

6. Which is bigger?

$191,000

$190,999

7. Which is the biggest?

$8,105

$8,051

$8,015

8. Which is the biggest?

$60,527

$60,335

$60,611

9. Put these amounts in order, smallest to largest.

$4,301 $4,134 $4,295

_____ smallest

_____ middle

_____ largest

10. Put these amounts in order.

$28,157 $29,575 $28,377

_____ smallest

_____ middle

_____ largest

9 COUNTING DOLLARS

To count dollars start with the biggest. (You did the same with small change.) Then add the next biggest. And so on.
Try to do it in your head.

ten dollars
(+ $10) = twenty dollars
(+ $5) = twenty-five dollars
(+ $1) = twenty-six dollars
(+ $1) = twenty-seven dollars

Exercises

1.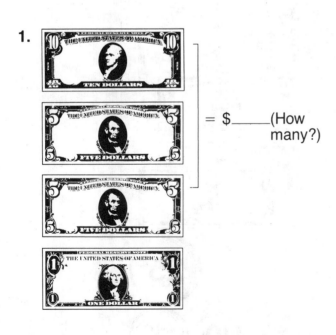
= $_____(How many?)

2.
= $_____

3.  = $_____

4. = $_____

5. = _____
(Don't forget the decimal!)

6. 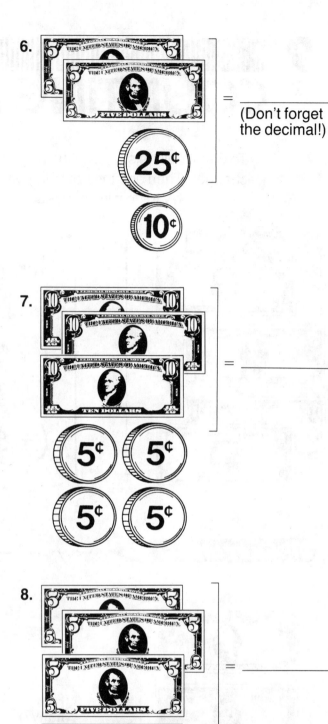 = _____
(Don't forget the decimal!)

7. = _____

8. = _____

10 REVIEW

1. $79 = _____-_____ _____ (Spell it out.)

2. Thirty-eight dollars = _____ (Dollar sign!)

3. Match. (Draw lines to connect the right answers.)

   $ 2,300   twenty-three thousand dollars
   $ 23,000   twenty-three hundred dollars

4. Match.

   $181,000   one hundred eighty-one thousand dollars
   $18,100   eighteen thousand one hundred dollars

5. Put the comma in the right place.

   $82005

6. Put the comma in the right place.

   $118355

7. Forty-six thousand, two hundred dollars = _____ (Don't forget the dollar sign and comma!)

8. Two hundred thousand, three hundred five dollars = _____

9. $6,311 = _____ (Spell it out.)

10. $150,000 = _____

11. Which is bigger? (Circle your answer.)

    $65,155
    $65,405

12. Which is bigger?

    $803,508
    $803,520

13. Which is biggest?

$1,106

$1,016

$1,061

14. Which is biggest?

$90,811

$91,118

$90,830

15. Put these amounts in order.

$7,520 $7,633 $7,921

_____ smallest

_____ middle

_____ largest

16. Put these amounts in order.

$50,588 $50,509 $53,366

_____ smallest

_____ middle

_____ largest

17. Fourteen dollars and twenty-seven cents

= _____

(Don't forget the dollar sign and decimal!)

18. Four hundred fifty-five dollars and seventy cents = _____

(Dollar sign and decimal!)

19. Five thousand, fifty-five dollars and seventy cents = _____

(Dollar sign, comma, and decimal!)

20. Seven thousand, two hundred thirty-three dollars and ten cents =

_____

21. Fifty thousand, one hundred dollars and ninety cents = _____

22.

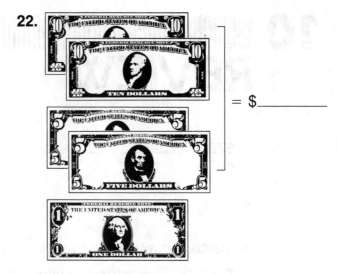

= $_____

23.

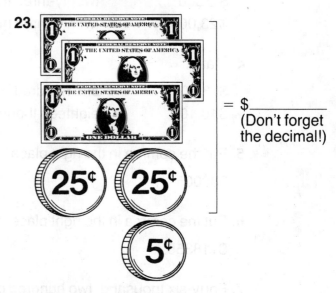

= $_____
(Don't forget the decimal!)

24.

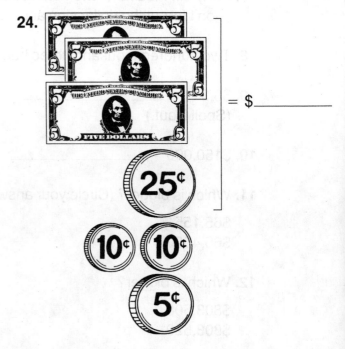

= $_____

SECTION B

11 ADDING DOLLAR AMOUNTS

Do you remember how to "carry" when you add? Let's review.

Example 1. Add $47 + $5

First you add the 7 + 5. ⟶
$$\$\ 47 \\ +\ 5$$

7 + 5 = 12. "Carry" the 1 (so you can add it to 4)—and write the 2. ⟶
$$\overset{1}{\$\ 47} \\ +\ 5 \\ \hline 2$$

Finish adding. Add the 1 you carried to the 4. ⟶
$$\overset{1}{\$\ 47} \\ +\ 5 \\ \hline \$\ 52$$

Example 2. Add $81 + $9

1 + 9 = 10. Carry the 1— write the 0. ⟶
$$\overset{1}{\$\ 81} \\ +\ 9 \\ \hline 0$$

Finish adding. Add the 1 you carried to the 8. ⟶

Note—You don't have to write the 1 you carry. You may want to keep it in your head.
$$\overset{1}{\$\ 81} \\ +\ 9 \\ \hline \$\ 90$$

1. $39
   + 2

(Don't forget the $ sign!)

2. $24
   + 7

3. $56
   + 2

(You don't have to "carry" in this one.)

4. $75
   + 9

5. $31
   + 3

6. $89
   + 2

7. $29
   + 1

8. $11
   + 9

9. $48
   + 3

10. $14
   + 5

11. $59
   + 4

12. $74
   + 9

13. $28
   + 2

14. $78
   + 5

15. $66
   + 6

16. $28
   + 9

17. $15
   + 7

18. $47
   + 7

19. $83
   + 9

20. $39
   + 8

12 ADDING DOLLARS AND CENTS

How do you add $7.53 + $1.25?

First **line everything up**

    Line up the decimals.
    Line up the numbers.
    Write in the $ signs.

(Note: You only have to write $ signs at the top and bottom.)

$$\begin{array}{r} \$7.53 \\ +\ 1.25 \\ \hline \$ \end{array}$$

    Now you can add.

$$\begin{array}{r} \$7.53 \\ +\ 1.25 \\ \hline \$8.78 \end{array}$$

Second example: Add $5.93 + $.71.

Line everything up. Then add 3 + 1 = 4	$\begin{array}{r} \$5.9\mathbf{3} \\ +\ .7\mathbf{1} \\ \hline \$\ .\ \mathbf{4} \end{array}$
9 + 7 = 16 (Carry the 1 and write the 6 below the line.)	$\begin{array}{r} {}^{1}\ \ \ \\ \$5.\mathbf{9}3 \\ +\ .71 \\ \hline \$\ .\mathbf{6}4 \end{array}$
5 + the 1 you carried = 6	$\begin{array}{r} {}^{1}\ \ \ \\ \$\mathbf{5}.93 \\ +\ .71 \\ \hline \$\mathbf{6}.64 \end{array}$

1. $ 2.26
+ .53

(Don't forget the $ sign!)

2. $ 1.45
+ 1.32

(Don't forget $ sign and decimal!)

3. $ 9.17
.50

4. $ 2.25
.09

(Remember to "carry.")

5. $ 5.48
2.23

6. Which is lined up properly?
Circle a. or b.

a) $ 6.60
+ .55
$7.15

b) $ 6.60
+ .55
$71.5

7. Which is lined up properly?

a) $ 14.78
+ 1.21
$15.99

b) $ 14.78
1.21
$26.88

8. Write these amounts. Line them up. Then add.
$3.24 + $.45

9. Line up these amounts. Then add.
$6.05 + $2.14

10. Add $2.26 + $6.68.

13 ADDING TOGETHER THREE DOLLAR AMOUNTS

To add together three or more dollar amounts, do the same things you've learned to do.

Line up decimals and numbers.

$$\begin{array}{r} \$\ 2.26 \\ 4.05 \\ +\ 1.53 \\ \hline \$\quad . \end{array}$$

"Carry" when you have to. (For example: last column: 6 + 5 + 3 = 14—carry 1, write the 4.)

$$\begin{array}{r} \overset{1}{} \\ \$\ 2.26 \\ 4.05 \\ +\ 1.53 \\ \hline \$\ 7.84 \end{array}$$

Exercises

1. $ 1.03
      3.15
   + .21

2. $ 3.65
      2.01
   + 4.25

3. $ 7.20
     .75
    .50
_____

(Remember to carry when you add
2 + 7 + 5.)

4. $ 4.21
   1.32
+ .60
_____

5. Line up these amounts. Then add.
$2.05 + $6.21 + $.33

6. Line up these amounts. Then add.
$4.44 + $.07 + $1.16

7. Add:
$1.90 + $3.07 + $2.91

8. Add:
$7.27 + $.09 + $.42

9. Add:
$5.75 + $2.25 + $1.11
(Note that you "carry" twice in this
problem.)

10. Add:
$1.94 + $3.76 + $.05

29

14 SUBTRACTING DOLLAR AMOUNTS

Do you remember how to "borrow" when you subtract?

Example 1. Subtract $73 − $9.

You can't subtract 9 from 3.
So you "borrow" 1 from the 7
in the next column.

Reduce the 7 to 6.

Increase the 3 to 13.

Now you can subtract.

$$\begin{array}{r} \overset{6}{\cancel{7}}\overset{13}{\cancel{3}} \\ \$ \\ -9 \\ \hline \end{array}$$

$$\begin{array}{r} \$\overset{6}{\cancel{7}}\overset{13}{\cancel{3}} \\ -9 \\ \hline \$\,64 \end{array}$$

Note—You don't always have to write down the
numbers you're borrowing. If you can, keep
them in your head.

Exercises

1. $\begin{array}{r} \$\ 53 \\ -\ 9 \\ \hline \end{array}$

2. $\begin{array}{r} \$\ 62 \\ -\ 8 \\ \hline \end{array}$

3. $\begin{array}{r} \$\ 55 \\ -\ 6 \\ \hline \end{array}$

4. $\begin{array}{r} \$\ 38 \\ -\ 7 \\ \hline \end{array}$

(You don't have to "borrow" in this one.)

5. $\begin{array}{r} \$\ 84 \\ -16 \\ \hline \end{array}$

6. $\begin{array}{r} \$\ 96 \\ -47 \\ \hline \end{array}$

7. $\begin{array}{r} \$545 \\ -\ 43 \\ \hline \end{array}$

8. $\begin{array}{r} \$485 \\ -\ 75 \\ \hline \end{array}$

9. $\begin{array}{r} \$377 \\ -\ 49 \\ \hline \end{array}$

10. $\begin{array}{r} \$711 \\ -209 \\ \hline \end{array}$

15 SUBTRACTING DOLLARS AND CENTS

How do you subtract $3.19 − $1.56?

First *line up the numbers and decimals*. Then subtract. *Borrow* if you have to.

To subtract 1 − 5, borrow from the 3 (next column). Reduce the 3 to 2. Increase the 1 to 11.

$$\begin{array}{r} \overset{2}{\cancel{3}}\,\overset{11}{\cancel{1}}9 \\ \$3.19 \\ -1.56 \\ \hline \$1.63 \end{array}$$

Exercises

1. $ 8.33
    − 5.21

2. $ 8.33
    − 5.41

(Remember to "borrow.")

3. $ 6.19
    − 4.28

4. $19.25
    − 3.09

5. $27.77
    − 8.00

6. Which is lined up properly? Circle a or b.

a) $ 90.03
   − 9.25
   $ .798

b) $ 90.03
   − 9.25
   $ 80.78

7. Which is lined up properly?

a) $111.99
   −109.79
   $ 2.20

b) $111.99
   −109.79
   $ 12.20

8. Subtract:
$36.65 − $7.00
(Be sure to line them up first.)

9. Subtract:
$80.28 − $2.25

10. Subtract:
$744.00 − $131.10

31

16 ||||||||||||||||||||||||||||||||||||||||||||||||||||||||||||||||||||
REVIEW

1. $ 45
    + 6

(Write your $ sign. Remember to carry.)

2. $ 84
    + 8

3. $ 77
    + 18

4. $ 28
    + 71

5. $5.27
    + .05

(Don't forget $ sign and decimal.)

6. $3.58
    + .61

7. Which is lined up properly?
Circle a. or b.

a) $ 75.88
   − 9.37
   $ 62.18

b) $ 75.88
   − 9.37
   $ 66.51

8. Which is lined up properly?

a) $ 418.30
   + 45.99
   $ 464.29

b) $ 418.30
   + 45.99
   $ 46.429

9. Line up these amounts. Then add:
$3.79 + $5.00

10. Add:
$12.75 + $9.04

11. Add:
$1.50 + $2.25 + $3.00

12. Add:
$4.90 + $4.90 + $.15

13. Add:
$1.28 + $1.09 + $7.51

14. $98
    − 9

(Remember to borrow.)

15. $31
    − 18

16. $ 652
    − 246

17. $2.77
    − .85

18. $94.00
    − 93.30

19. Subtract:
$23.59 − $11.61
(Be sure to line them up first.)

20. Subtract:
$286.88 − $100.19

17 MULTIPLYING DOLLAR AMOUNTS

You know that

$$\begin{array}{r} \$6 \\ \times 3 \\ \hline \$18 \end{array}$$

How much is $26 × 3?

First multiply 3 × 6 = 18
Carry the 1 (in 18) so you can
add it in later)—and write the
8.

$$\begin{array}{r} \overset{1}{} \\ \$26 \\ \times 3 \\ \hline \$\ 8 \end{array}$$

Next multiply 3 × 2 = 6.
Add the 1 you carried. Your
answer is 7. Write it down.

$26 × 3 = $78

$$\begin{array}{r} \overset{1}{} \\ \$26 \\ \times 3 \\ \hline \$78 \end{array}$$

Second example. $36 × 2.

First multiply 2 × 6 = 12
Carry the 1, write 2

$$\begin{array}{r} \overset{1}{} \\ \$36 \\ \times 2 \\ \hline \$\ 2 \end{array}$$

Next multiply 2 × 3 = 6
Add the 1 you carried = 7

$$\begin{array}{r} \overset{1}{} \\ \$36 \\ \times 2 \\ \hline \$72 \end{array}$$

Third example. $33 × 5

Muliply 5 × 3 = 15.
Carry.
Then multiply 5 × 3 again =
15. Add 15 + 1 (which you
carried) = 16. Write it down.

$$\begin{array}{r} \overset{1}{} \\ \$33 \\ \times 5 \\ \hline \$165 \end{array}$$

1. $15
  × 3
———

5. $23
  × 3
———

8. $54
  × 2
———

(This time, you don't have to carry.)

2. $27
  × 2
———

6. $12
  × 7
———

9. $56
  × 2
———

3. $39
  × 2
———

7. $50
  × 2
———

10. $75
  × 3
———

4. $24
  × 4
———

18 MULTIPLYING DOLLARS AND CENTS

Example 1.

Note where the decimal goes.

$$\begin{array}{r} \$\ 3.10 \\ \times\ 3 \\ \hline \$\ 9.30 \end{array}$$

Example 2.

Again, note the decimal.

$$\begin{array}{r} \$\ 3.10 \\ \times\ 4 \\ \hline \$12.40 \end{array}$$

Example 3.

This time, you have to carry.
Again, note the decimal.

$$\begin{array}{r} \$\ 2.52 \\ \times\ 4 \\ \hline \$10.08 \end{array}$$

Exercises

1. $\begin{array}{r} \$\ 3.72 \\ \times\ \ \ 2 \\ \hline \end{array}$

3. $\begin{array}{r} \$\ 5.71 \\ \times\ \ \ 2 \\ \hline \end{array}$

5. $\begin{array}{r} \$\ 9.03 \\ \times\ \ \ 3 \\ \hline \end{array}$

(Remember to carry. And be sure to put in the $ sign and decimal.)

4. $\begin{array}{r} \$\ 9.00 \\ \times\ \ \ 3 \\ \hline \end{array}$

6. $\begin{array}{r} \$\ 9.05 \\ \times\ \ \ 3 \\ \hline \end{array}$

2. $\begin{array}{r} \$\ 4.63 \\ \times\ \ \ 2 \\ \hline \end{array}$

7. $11.42
×   4

9. $20.19
×   4

(4 × 9 is 36. This time
you carry 3.)

8. $ 1.72
×   3

10. $26.05
×   3

(3 × 7 = 21. This time you
carry 2.)

19 ‖‖‖‖‖‖‖‖‖‖‖‖‖‖‖‖‖‖‖‖‖‖‖‖‖‖‖‖‖‖‖‖
DIVIDING DOLLARS

$25 divided by 4 ⎤
$25 ÷ 4   ⎬   These all mean the same thing. Let's do this problem step by step.
4 into $25   ⎦

Step 1. Set up the problem. Put the dollar sign directly above the other dollar sign.

$$4\overline{)\$25}$$

Step 2. Does 4 divide into 2? *No*. Don't write anything. Go to next step.

Step 3. The 2 was too small. So try dividing 4 into 25. Does 4 divide into 25? *Yes*. 6 times. Write the 6 above the 25.

$$4\overline{)\$25}^{\ \ 6}$$

Step 4. Multiply 6 × 4 = 24. Write 24 below 25.

$$4\overline{)\$25}^{\ \ 6}\ \ 24$$

Step 5. Subtract. You get 1. This is called your remainder or R1. In this case it equals ¼, or $.25

$$\begin{array}{r} \$\ \ 6 \\ 4\overline{)\$25} \\ 24 \\ \hline 1 \end{array}$$

Second example. 76 ÷ 3

Step 1. 3 into 7 goes 2 times. Write 2 above the 6.

$$3\overline{)\$76}^{\$2}$$

Step 2. Multiply 2 × 3 = 6. Subtract 6 from 7 = 1.

$$\begin{array}{r} \$2 \\ 3\overline{)\$76} \\ 6 \\ \hline 1 \end{array}$$

(Example continued on next page.)

Step 3. Bring down your 6. Now you have sixteen on this line.

$$3\overline{)\,\$76}$$
$$\,\$2$$
$$6$$
$$16$$

Step 4. Divide 3 into 16. It goes 5 times. Write 5 above the 6. →

$$3\overline{)\,\$76}$$
$$\,\$25$$
$$6$$
$$16$$

Step 5. Multiply 5 × 3 = 15. Subtract 15 from 16 = 1. 1 is your remainder (or ⅓, about $.33)

$$3\overline{)\,\$76}$$
$$\,\$25$$
$$6$$
$$16$$
$$15$$
$$1$$

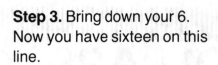 **Exercises**

1.

$$4\overline{)\,\$9}$$

(Do you get a remainder? How much?)

2.

$$3\overline{)\,\$33}$$

(No remainder in this one. —Don't forget your dollar sign.)

3.

$$5\overline{)\,\$16}$$

(How big was your remainder?)

4.

$$2\overline{)\,\$30}$$

5.

$$7\overline{)\,\$16}$$

6.

$$9\overline{)\,\$28}$$

7.

$$6\overline{)\,\$65}$$

8.

$$6\overline{)\,\$665}$$

9.

$$5\overline{)\,\$205}$$

10.

$$4\overline{)\,\$321}$$

20 DIVIDING DOLLARS AND CENTS

Example. 4)$9.75

Step 1. Put in $ sign and decimal. Line them up *directly* above the ones below.

$$\begin{array}{r} \$ \\ 4\overline{)\$9.75} \end{array}$$

Step 2. Divide 4 into 9 goes 2 times. Write 2. Multiply. Subtract. Bring down the 7.

$$\begin{array}{r} \$2 \\ 4\overline{)\$9.75} \\ \underline{8} \\ 17 \end{array}$$

Step 3. 4 into 17 goes 4 times. Multiply. Subtract. Bring down the 5.

$$\begin{array}{r} \$2.4 \\ 4\overline{)\$9.75} \\ \underline{8} \\ 17 \\ \underline{16} \\ 15 \end{array}$$

Step 4. 4 into 15 goes 3 times. Multiply. Subtract. Remainder is 3.

$$\begin{array}{r} \$2.43 \\ 4\overline{)\$9.75} \\ \underline{8} \\ 17 \\ \underline{16} \\ 15 \\ \underline{12} \\ 3 \end{array}$$

The answer is $2.43 with a remainder of 3, or ¾ of a cent.

1. $\dfrac{\$\qquad.\qquad}{4\overline{)\$8.05}}$

6. $9\overline{)\$8.10}$

2. $\dfrac{\$\qquad.\qquad}{6\overline{)\$12.00}}$

7. $7\overline{)\$30.05}$

3. $7\overline{)\$21.00}$

8. $8\overline{)\$81.73}$

(Remember to put in $ sign and decimal!)

4. $5\overline{)\$4.50}$

9. $3\overline{)\$43.71}$

5. $2\overline{)\$17.23}$

10. $4\overline{)\$39.05}$

21 REVIEW

1. $26
   × 3

2. $19
   × 2

3. $17
   × 5

4. $62
   × 6

5. $1.19
   ×   2

6. $7.04
   ×   4

7. $2.61
   ×   4

8. $11.81
   ×   6

9. $25.09
   ×   3

10. $10.34
    ×   4

11. 5)$19

12. 4)$48

13. 3)$69

14. 7)$210

15. 6)$511

16. 3)$6.06

(Remember $ sign and decimal!)

17. 4)$3.35

18. 8)$8.94

19. 4)$32.43

20. 5)$45.45

41

SECTION C

22 ROUNDING AND ESTIMATING

You want to buy 2 pairs of slacks. One costs $19.95. The other costs $24.95. About how much money will you need to buy them both?

The quickest way to figure it is to round $19.95 and $24.95 to the nearest dollars and add.

> $19.95 rounded to the nearest dollar = $20
> $24.95 rounded = $25

$$\begin{array}{r} \$20 \\ +\ 25 \\ \hline \$45 \end{array}$$

You will need about $45 (plus a few dollars for the sales tax if there is one where you live).

Second example. About how much is $310.59 times 4?

The quick way to figure this one is to round $310.59 to the nearest $10. Then multiply.

> $310.59 rounded to nearest $10 = $310.
> (In this case, you round *down* to $310, since you are closer to $310 than $320.)

$$\begin{array}{r} \$310 \\ \times\ 4 \\ \hline \$1{,}240 \end{array}$$

$310.59 × 4 is *about* $1240.

Exercises

1. Round and estimate.

$7.90 rounded = $ ___
+ 9.03 rounded = + ___
$

2. Round and estimate.

$19.83 rounded = $ ___
+ 20.99 rounded = + ___
$

3. Round and estimate.

$3.05 + $85.95

$
+
$

4. Round and estimate.

$110.30 + $6.92

5. Round and estimate.

$18.88 + $18.88

8. Round and estimate.

$402 × 9

6. Round and estimate.

$299.99 × 3

9. Round and estimate.

$896 × 4

7. Round and estimate.

$50.38 × 6

10. Round and estimate.

$199 **divided by** 2

23 ADDING AND SUBTRACTING DOLLARS ON A CALCULATOR

Look at this calculator:

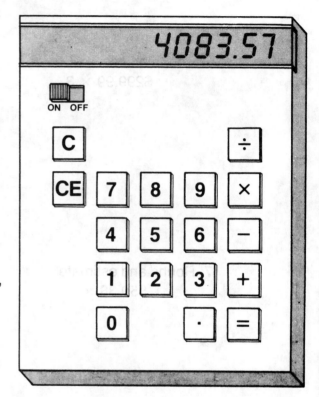

Find the following buttons:
- **+** (to add)
- **−** (to subtract)
- **.** (decimal point)
- **CE** (means "clear entry"—to erase a mistake)
- **C** (means "clear"—to erase everything, when you want to start over. You may want to press C when you start a problem, to make sure the calculator is clear.)
- **=** (to find your answer)

Example 1. Add $73 + $129 + $85 on the calculator

Press 73

Press +

Press 129

Press +

Press 85

Press =

The calculator tells you your answer is $287. (You put in the $ sign.)

46

Example 2. Subtract $988 − $293 on the calculator

Press   **988**

Press   **—**

Press   **292**

(OOPS! Sorry, we made a mistake!)

Press   **CE (to "clear" the 292 "entry")**

Press   **293 (the correct buttons)**

Press   **=**

The calculator tells you your answer is $695.

Note: We've shown the way a typical calculator works. Some calculators work a little differently. Before you start working on a calculator, be sure you find out how it works.

Exercises

1. Subtract $355 − $276 on the calculator.
Press 355
Press ___ (which button?)
Press 276
Press ___ (which button?)

The calculator will tell you your answer is $79.

2. Add $43 + $199 + $465 on the calculator.
Press 43
Press +
Press ___
Press ___ } Which buttons?
Press ___
Press ___

The calculator will tell you your answer is $707.

3. Subtract $1,200 − $705 on the calculator
Press ___
Press ___
Press ___
Press ___

The calculator will tell you your answer is $495.

4. Add $321 + $10 + $690 on the calculator.
Press ___
Press ___
Press ___
Press ___
Press ___
Press ___

The calculator will tell you your answer is $1,021.

5. Subtract $3,082 − $1,677 on the calculator.

Press ____

Press ____

Press ____

Press ____

The calculator will tell you your answer is $1,405.

6. Subtract $4,440 − $295 on the calculator.

____

____

____

____

The calculator will tell you your answer is $4,145.

7. Add $27 + $150 + $99 on the calculator.

____

____

____

____

____

____

The calculator will tell you your answer is $276.

8. Subtract $10,000 − $1,302 on the calculator.

____

____

____

____

The calculator will tell you your answer is $8,698.

9. You're adding several dollar amounts on the calculator. The last one is $7,816. You press $8,716 by mistake. What button do you press to "clear" your error? (Without erasing everything else.)

____

10. On another calculator problem, you realize you have made several mistakes. What button do you press to start over?

____

24 ADDING AND SUBTRACTING DOLLARS AND CENTS ON A CALCULATOR

Once again, find the following buttons:

+
−
•
CE
C
=

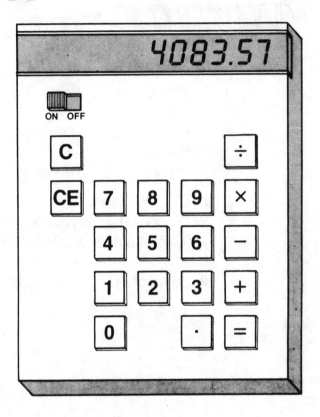

Example. Add $3.88 + $22 + $7.60 + $.39 on the calculator.

Press 3.88
Press +
Press 22
Press +
Press 7.60   (Example continued next page.)

Press +
Press .39
Press =

The calculator will tell you your answer is $33.87.

◖▮▮ Exercises ◗⟩ ～⟋⟍

1. Add $18.88 + $.99 + $2 on the calculator.
   Press_____(Include decimal.)
   Press_____
   Press_____(Decimal.)
   Press_____
   Press_____(No decimal.)
   Press_____

   Did you put in all your decimals? If you did the problem correctly, the calculator will tell you your answer is $21.87.

2. Subtract $185.50 − $135 on the calculator.
   _____
   _____
   _____
   _____

   The calculator will tell you your answer is $50.50.

3. You want to start a problem over.
   Press ____

4. You forget a decimal in one of the dollar amounts in a long list you are adding. To correct the error (but not erase everything)—
   Press ____

5. Add $2,015.17 + $6,632.63 on the calculator.
   _____
   _____
   _____
   _____

   The calculator will tell you your answer is $8,647.80.

6. Add $49 + $89 + $1.75 on the calculator.

_____

_____

_____

_____ (Watch the decimal!)

_____

The calculator will tell you your answer is $139.75.

7. Subtract $824 − $6.99 on the calculator.

_____

_____

_____

_____

The calculator will tell you your answer is $817.01.

8. Add $5.99 + $7.99 + $12 on the calculator.

_____

_____

_____

_____

_____

_____

The calculator will tell you your answer is $25.98.

9. Subtract $175.33 − $76 on the calculator.

_____

_____

_____

_____

The calculator will tell you your answer is $99.33.

10. You are about to start a problem on the calculator. The calculator shows a number on the screen. It is left over from an earlier problem. What do you do before you start your problem?

_____

25 ▌▌
MULTIPLYING AND DIVIDING MONEY ON A CALCULATOR

Find the following buttons:

$\times$ (to multiply)

$\div$ (to divide)

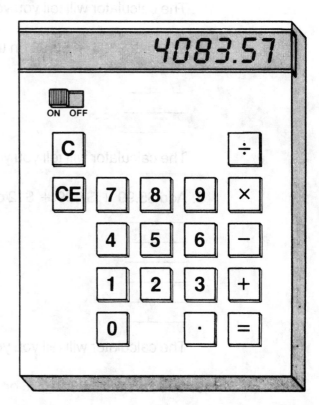

Example 1. Multiply $49.50 $\times$ 8 on the calculator.

Press $49.5 (You don't have to press the final 0 after the decimal.)

Press $\times$

Press 8

Press =

The calculator will tell you your answer is $396.

Example 2. Divide $73.87 by 14 on the calculator.

Press 73.87

Press $\div$

Press 14

Press =

The calculator will tell you your answer is $5.27 followed by a string of numbers. You "round off" to $5.28.

Exercises

1. Multiply $703.99 × 20 on the calculator.
   Press ____
   Press ____
   Press ____
   Press ____

   The calculator will tell you your answer is $14,079.80.

2. Divide $13.50 by 6 on the calculator.
   Press ____
   Press ____
   Press ____
   Press ____

   The calculator will tell you your answer is $2.25.

3. Multiply $17.75 × 11 on the calculator.
   ____
   ____
   ____
   ____

   The calculator will tell you your answer is $195.25.

4. Divide $1,307.06 by 3 on the calculator.
   ____
   ____
   ____
   ____

   The calculator will tell you your answer is $435.68 followed by a string of numbers. You round to $435.69.

5. Multiply $83.33 × 206 on the calculator.
   ____
   ____
   ____
   ____

   The calculator will tell you your answer is $17,165.98.

6. Divide $5,550.10 by 9 on the calculator.
   ____
   ____
   ____
   ____

   The calculator will tell you your answer is $616.68 (after you've rounded the last penny).

26 |||||||||||||||||||||||||||||||||||||||||||||||||||||||||||
REVIEW

1. Round and estimate.

$14.10 rounded = $ _____

+ 23.95 rounded = + _____

$

2. Round and estimate.

$397 rounded = $ _____

× _____5

$

3. Round and estimate.

$55.85 + $31.02

$

+   _____

$

4. Round and estimate.

$8.97 + $13.85

5. Round and estimate.

$303 × 4

6. Subtract $1,103 − $87.50 on a calculator.

Press _____

Press _____

Press _____

Press _____

The calculator will tell you your answer is
$1,015.50.

7. Multiply $316.12 × 5 on the calculator.

_____

_____

_____

_____

The calculator will tell you your answer is
$1,580.60.

8. Divide $877.33 by 4 on the calculator.

_____

_____

_____

_____

The calculator will tell you your answer is
$219.33 (rounded).

9. Add $150.75 + $1,827 on the calculator.

_____

_____

_____

_____

The calculator will tell you your answer is
$1,977.75.

10. Add $6.10 + $22 + $15.55 on the calculator.

_____

_____

_____

_____

_____

The calculator will tell you your answer is
$43.65.

27 NUMBER, SIZE, AND PRICE

You want to compare the prices of 2 different brands of soup in the supermarket.

Brand A is marked 3 cans for $1.00.
Brand B is marked 27¢ each.

Which is cheaper *per can*?

To find out, first figure the **price per can** for Brand A.

$$3 \overline{)\begin{array}{l} \$\ .33 \\ \$1.00 \\ \underline{99} \\ 1 \end{array}}$$

or $.33⅓ = $.34, since the store will round up to the next penny if you only buy one can.

Brand A costs $.34 per can.
Brand B costs 27¢ each = $.27.
Brand B is cheaper.

Second example
Many stores price things as shown below. This is called unit pricing.
It is done to help you compare prices. Let's look.

Brand A

UNIT PRICE	WT.	PRICE THIS PKG.
$.53 /oz.	6 oz.	$3.19

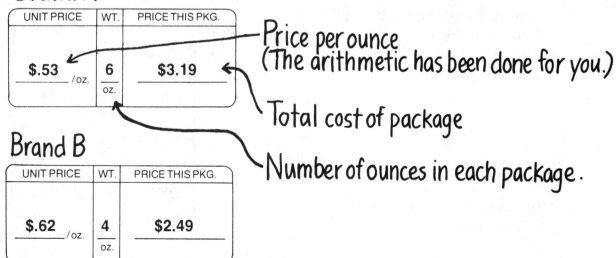

Price per ounce
(The arithmetic has been done for you.)

Total cost of package

Number of ounces in each package.

Brand B

UNIT PRICE	WT.	PRICE THIS PKG.
$.62 /oz.	4 oz.	$2.49

55

Brand A is cheaper per ounce ($.53 versus $.62).

Example 3. Brand A tires 2 for $48. Brand B tires 4 for $88. Which is cheaper per tire?

Here you have to divide in both cases.

$$2\overline{)\$48}^{\$24} \qquad 4\overline{)\$88}^{\$22}$$

Brand A costs $24 each. Brand B costs $22 each. Brand B is cheaper.

Exercises

1. Which is cheaper per box? Circle A or B.

    A. 3 boxes for $.39   Do your arithmetic
    B. $.19 each   here:

2. Which is cheaper per can?

    A. 2 cans for $.99 (Round $.99 to $1.00
       before you divide.)
    B. 59¢ each

3. Which is cheaper per yard?

    A. 10 yards for $18
    B. $1.50 per yard

4. Which is cheaper per ounce?

A.

UNIT PRICE	WT.	PRICE THIS PKG.
$.17 /oz.	6 oz.	$1.02

B.

UNIT PRICE	WT.	PRICE THIS PKG.
$.23 /oz.	4 oz.	$.92

5. Which is cheaper per pound?

A.

UNIT PRICE	WT.	PRICE THIS PKG.
$.81 /lb.	6 lbs.	$4.86

B.

UNIT PRICE	WT.	PRICE THIS PKG.
$.88 /lb.	5 lbs.	$4.40

6. Which is cheaper per can?

    A. 2 cans for $.88
    B. 3 cans for $.99

9. Which is cheaper per bottle?

    A. 6 for $2.89
    B. 6 for $3.59

    Note: Look at this problem again, before you do a lot of extra work.

7. Which is cheaper per container?

    A. 2 for $.59
    B. 4 for $1.00

10. Which is cheaper per pair of sox?

    A. 6 pairs for $5.99
    B. 2 pairs for $2.99

    (Round up on this one, to $6 in A and to $3 in B before you divide.)

8. Which is cheaper per pound?

A.

UNIT PRICE	WT.	PRICE THIS PKG.
$.25 /lb.	7 lbs.	$1.75

B. 5 pounds for $1.49.

28 USING MONEY TABLES

A customer buys an item for $.95. There is a sales tax where she lives. How much is the tax?

One way to figure it out is go to a sales tax table. Sales tax tables are different, depending on what per cent the tax is. The sales tax table for the area where the $.95 purchase was made is shown below.

$.95 is between $.84 and $.99 (see circled area). Sales tax is $.06.

Second example. What is the sales tax on this tax table for a purchase of $44.25?

$44.25 is between $44.24 and $44.38 (see the area inside the thick black lines). Sales tax is $2.88.

Transaction	Tax	Transaction	Tax	Transaction	Tax	Transaction	Tax	Transaction	Tax
.01– .10	.00	14.24–14.38	.93	28.54–28.69	1.86	42.85–42.99	2.79	57.16–57.30	3.72
.11– .20	.01	14.39–14.53	.94	28.70–28.84	1.87	43.00–43.15	2.80	57.31–57.46	3.73
.21– .35	.02	14.54–14.69	.95	28.85–28.99	1.88	43.16–43.30	2.81	57.47–57.61	3.74
.36– .51	.03	14.70–14.84	.96	29.00–29.15	1.89	43.31–43.46	2.82	57.62–57.76	3.75
.52– .67	.04	14.85–14.99	.97	29.16–29.30	1.90	43.47–43.61	2.83	57.77–57.92	3.76
.68– .83	.05	15.00–15.15	.98	29.31–29.46	1.91	43.62–43.76	2.84	57.93–58.07	3.77
.84– .99	.06	15.16–15.30	.99	29.47–29.61	1.92	43.77–43.92	2.85	58.08–58.23	3.78
1.00– 1.15	.07	15.31–15.46	1.00	29.62–29.76	1.93	43.93–44.07	2.86	58.24–58.38	3.79
1.16– 1.30	.08	15.47–15.61	1.01	29.77–29.92	1.94	44.08–44.23	2.87	58.39–58.53	3.80
1.31– 1.46	.09	15.62–15.76	1.02	29.93–30.07	1.95	44.24–44.38	2.88	58.54–58.69	3.81
1.47– 1.61	.10	15.77–15.92	1.03	30.08–30.23	1.96			58.70–58.84	3.82
1.62– 1.76	.11	15.93–16.07	1.04	30.24–30.38	1.97	44.54–44.69	2.90	58.85–58.99	3.83
1.77– 1.92	.12	16.08–16.23	1.05	30.39–30.53	1.98	44.70–44.84	2.91	59.00–59.15	3.84
1.93– 2.07	.13	16.24–16.38	1.06	30.54–30.69	1.99	44.85–44.99	2.92	59.16–59.30	3.85
2.08– 2.23	.14	16.39–16.53	1.07	30.70–30.84	2.00	45.00–45.15	2.93	59.31–59.46	3.86
2.24 2.38	.15	16.54 16.69	1.08	30.85 30.99	2.01	45.16 45.30	2.94	59.47 59.61	3.87

58

Use the sales tax table to find the answers to all of the following questions.

Transaction	Tax	Transaction	Tax	Transaction	Tax
.01– .10	.00	14.24–14.38	.93	28.54–28.69	1.86
.11– .20	.01	14.39–14.53	.94	28.70–28.84	1.87
.21– .35	.02	14.54–14.69	.95	28.85–28.99	1.88
.36– .51	.03	14.70–14.84	.96	29.00–29.15	1.89
.52– .67	.04	14.85–14.99	.97	29.16–29.30	1.90
.68– .83	.05	15.00–15.15	.98	29.31–29.46	1.91
.84– .99	.06	15.16–15.30	.99	29.47–29.61	1.92
1.00– 1.15	.07	15.31–15.46	1.00	29.62–29.76	1.93
1.16– 1.30	.08	15.47–15.61	1.01	29.77–29.92	1.94
1.31– 1.46	.09	15.62–15.76	1.02	29.93–30.07	1.95
1.47– 1.61	.10	15.77–15.92	1.03	30.08–30.23	1.96
1.62– 1.76	.11	15.93–16.07	1.04	30.24–30.38	1.97

1. On the tax table, $.75 is between $.68 and $_____.

What is the sales tax on $.75? (to the right.)_____

2. On the tax table, $30.10 is between $_____ and $_____.

What is the sales tax on $30.10? _____

3. The sales tax on $.40 is $_____.

4. The sales tax on $15.15 is $_____.

5. The sales tax on $29.88 is $_____.

For the following questions, use the postage chart.

```
FIRST CLASS

1 oz.......20        7 oz......1.22

2 " .......37        8 " ......1.39

3 " .......54        9 " ......1.56

4 " .......71       10 "......1.73

5 " .......88       11 "......1.90

6 " .....1.05       12 "......2.07
```

6. A letter weighs 3 ounces. Find 3 ounces on the postage chart. (It is circled.)

What is the 1st class postage? (To the right.) $_____

7. A package weights 8 ounces. What is the 1st class postage?
$_____

8. A package weights 11 ounces. What is the 1st class postage?
$_____

9. A letter weighs 2 ounces. What is the 1st class postage? $_____

10. A letter weighs 4 ounces. What is the 1st class postage? $_____

29 SALES TAX

The area where you live is likely to have a sales tax. Most sales taxes are from 2% to 8%.

How do you figure a sales tax? You learned in the last lesson that you may have a tax table to help you. But what if you don't have a tax table? You have to figure the tax yourself.

First change % to decimal. For example:

$$5\% = .05$$
$$6\% = .06$$
$$7\% = .07$$
$$8\% = .08$$

Now you can multiply.

Example 1. How much is a 6% tax on a $220 purchase? Multiply $220 × .06.

$$
\begin{array}{r}
\$220 \\
.06 \\
\hline
\$13.20
\end{array}
$$
2 decimals above
2 decimals below

The tax is $13.20.

Example 2. 5% tax on $10.80. Multiply $10.80 × .05.

$$
\begin{array}{r}
\$10.80 \\
\times .05 \\
\hline
\$.5400
\end{array}
$$
4 decimal places total here
4 decimal places here

$.5400 = $.54. The answer is $.54.

Want a quick way to do this problem? Use a calculator. Or use a tax table.

1. What is a 6% tax on $10? Show your multiplication below.

2. What is a 6% tax on $1? Show your multiplication below.

3. What is a 5% tax on $24?

4. What is a 5% tax on $1.20? (In your answer, be sure to put in *4* decimal places.)

$$\begin{array}{r} \$\ 1.20 \\ \times\ \ .05 \\ \hline \end{array}$$

5. What is an 8% tax on $4.50? (4 decimal places again.)

6. What is a 5% tax on $75? (Only 2 decimal places here.)

7. What is a 5% tax on $.90? (In this one, round your answer to next higher penny.)

8. What is a 4% tax on $2.90? (Again, round your answer to next higher penny.)

9. What is a 7% tax on $1.40?

10. What is a 5% tax on $10.92?

30 TIPS

How much do you tip the waiter when you have a meal in a restaurant? How much do you tip for a cab ride?

It's up to you. But you may want to base your tip on what people usually give in your area. In some areas, you are not expected to tip for a cab ride, or for service in certain kinds of restaurants.

In other situations, you are often expected to tip from about 10% of the bill to about 15%. How do you figure out the amount?

Do it in your head if you can. You don't have to figure it exactly.

Or if you want to, write it out.

Example 1. 10% Tips.

$$10\% \text{ tip on } \$1.00 = \$.10$$
$$10\% \text{ tip on } \$2.00 = \$.20$$
$$10\% \text{ tip on } \$10.00 = \$1.00$$
$$10\% \text{ tip on } \$1.20 = \$.12$$
$$10\% \text{ tip on } \$3.50 = \$.35$$

Do you get the idea? You may be able to do these in your head. If not, charge 10% to .10 and multiply. For example: $3.50 × .10.

$$
\begin{array}{r}
\$3.50 \\
\times .10 \\
\hline
\$.3500 \\
\end{array}
$$

4 decimal places

4 decimal places in answer

$$\$.3500 = \$.35$$

63

Example 2. What is a 12% tip on a $15.80 meal?

$$12\% = .12 \quad \text{Multiply } \$15.80 \times .12$$

$$
\begin{array}{r}
\$15.80 \\
\times\ .12 \\
\hline
3160 \\
1580 \\
\hline
\$1.8960
\end{array}
$$

4 decimal places

4 decimal places

Round your tip to next nickel = $1.90.

 **Exercises**

1. A meal costs you $5. What is a 10% tip on this meal? (You may be able to figure this one in your head.)

4. What is a 10% tip on $6.90? (Round this answer to next higher nickel.)

2. What is a 10% tip on $12?

5. What is a 10% tip on $7.35? (Again, round to next higher nickel.)

3. What is a 10% tip on $4.50?

6. What is a *12%* tip on a $10 meal?

7. What is a 15% tip on a $10 meal?

9. What is a 12% tip on $3?

8. What is a 15% tip on $20?

10. What is a 15% tip on a $5.95 meal? (The easiest way to do this is to round $5.95 to $6. Then multiply $\times$ .15.)

31 REVIEW

1. Which is cheaper per can? Circle A or B. Show your division for A.

   A. 2 cans for $.78
   B. $.35 each

2. Which is cheaper per pound?

   A. 4 pounds for $.99. (Make it easy on yourself. Round $.99 to $1 before you divide.)
   B. $.31 each

3. Which is cheaper per bottle?

   A. 3 for $1.69
   B. $.79 each

4. Which is cheaper per pound?

   A.
UNIT PRICE	WT.	PRICE THIS PKG.
$1.47 /lb.	6 lbs.	$8.82

   B.
UNIT PRICE	WT.	PRICE THIS PKG.
$1.63 /lb.	5 lbs.	$8.15

5. Which is cheaper per ounce?

   A.
UNIT PRICE	WT.	PRICE THIS PKG.
$.61 /oz.	1 oz.	$.61

   B.
UNIT PRICE	WT.	PRICE THIS PKG.
$.57 /oz.	5 oz.	$2.85

6. Which is cheaper per container?

   A. 2 containers for $.90
   B. 3 containers for $1.19

Use this sales tax table for questions 7 and 8.

Transaction	Tax	Transaction	Tax	Transaction	Tax	Transactio
.01– .10	.00	14.24–14.38	.93	28.54–28.69	1.86	42.85–42.9
.11– .20	.01	14.39–14.53	.94	28.70–28.84	1.87	43.00–43.1
.21– .35	.02	14.54–14.69	.95	28.85–28.99	1.88	43.16–43.3
.36– .51	.03	14.70–14.84	.96	29.00–29.15	1.89	43.31–43.4
.52– .67	.04	14.85–14.99	.97	29.16–29.30	1.90	43.47–43.6
.68– .83	.05	15.00–15.15	.98	29.31–29.46	1.91	43.62–43.7
.84– .99	.06	15.16–15.30	.99	29.47–29.61	1.92	43.77–43.9
1.00– 1.15	.07	15.31–15.46	1.00	29.62–29.76	1.93	43.93–44.0
1.16– 1.30	.08	15.47–15.61	1.01	29.77–29.92	1.94	44.08–44.2
1.31– 1.46	.09	15.62–15.76	1.02	29.93–30.07	1.95	44.24–44.3
1.47– 1.61	.10	15.77–15.99	1.03	30.08–30.23	1.96	44.39–44.5

7. What is the sales tax on the tax table above for a purchase of $14.60?

_____

8. What is the sales tax on the tax table for a purchase of $15.75?

_____

....

9. What is a 7% tax on a $10 purchase? _____

10. What is an 8% tax on a $20 purchase?_____

11. What is a 6% tax on $12?_____

12. What is a 5% tax on $.60? (Watch the decimal places in your answer.)_____

13. What is a 5% tax on $1.40?_____

14. What is a 6% tax on $.80? (In this one, round your answer to next higher penny.)_____

15. What is an 8% tax on $1.75? _____

16. What is a 10% tip on a $15 meal? _____

17. What is a 10% tip on a $7.50 meal? _____

18. What is a 10% tip on $3.40? (Round your answer to next higher nickel.) _____

19. What is a 15% tip on $5? _____

20. What is a 12% tip on $1.90? (Round answer to next higher nickel.)

_____

SECTION D

32 PETTY CASH EXPENSES

At work, people from time to time have to lay out small amounts of money on things they need on the job. Sometimes you spend your own money, and the company pays you back. Sometimes you are given money ahead of time. Then you give back the change from whatever you spend.

Example 1. Your boss gives you $6. She tells you to go out and buy a 9-volt battery ($1.25) and a pair of scissors ($4.60). What change do you bring back?

Step 1 Add $1.25 + $4.60

$$\begin{array}{r} \$1.25 \text{ battery} \\ 4.60 \text{ scissors} \\ \hline \$5.85 \end{array}$$

Step 2 Subtract the $5.85 from the $6.00 your boss gave you.

$$\begin{array}{r} \$6.00 \\ -5.85 \\ \hline \$.15 \end{array}$$

You bring back $.15. *Keep your receipts* so you can add up the amounts exactly!

Example 2. Most companies have "petty cash vouchers." They are simple forms. When you spend money on company business, you keep an exact list of what you spent. *Get receipts!* Then you fill out a petty cash slip and give it to the bookkeeper, along with all the receipts.

Mary Alonso handed in this petty cash voucher.

```
661-8/79                    YORK UNIVERSITY
INSTRUCTIONS:             PETTY CASH VOUCHER
  1. USE THIS FORM TO OBTAIN REIMBURSEMENT FOR ANY AUTHORIZED PETTY CASH
     EXPENDITURES.
  NOTE:
  EACH ORDER FOR SUPPLIES AND EQUIPMENT TOTALING MORE THAN $50.00 MUST
  BE REQUISITIONED THROUGH THE PURCHASING DIVISION OR OTHER CENTRAL
  SERVICE UNIT - STOCK ROOM, PRINT SHOP, ETC.
  2. PREPARE THIS FORM IN DUPLICATE.
  3. ORIGINAL RECEIPTS AND/OR RECEIPTED INVOICES MUST BE ATTACHED.
  4. PRESENT COPY #1 OF THIS APPROVED VOUCHER TO YOUR LOCAL FINANCE OFFICE.
                    PRINT OR TYPEWRITE
```

PAYEE NAME:		DATE
Mary Alonso		9/20

DEPARTMENT TO BE CHARGED:	ACCOUNT NUMBER			
	L	ACCT.	DEPT.	CODE
Production				

EXPLANATION	AMOUNT
4 rolls tape @ $.49	$ 1.96
Bus fares	1.50
Telephone call to office	.20

TOTAL AMOUNT OF REIMBURSEMENT IN WORDS:	TOTAL AMOUNT	
Three and 66/100 DOLLARS	$	3.66

APPROVAL SIGNATURE

Sandra Peale

DEAN OR HEAD OF ADMINISTRATIVE UNIT   DATE

                                                       TELLER
                                                       AND DATE

NAME OF PERSON TO PICK-UP CASH   (PRINT OR TYPE)

PAYEE'S SIGNATURE AUTHORIZING PERSON ABOVE TO PICK-UP CASH

```
SIGNATURE OF PERSON RECEIVING CASH    Date
To Be Signed in the Presence of the Teller    Copy #1 (White) Finance Office
or Departmental Petty Cash Fund Custodian.    Copy #2 (Pink) Dept. File
```

Note that Mary got 4 rolls of tape. Each cost $.49. She multipled 4 × $.49 = $1.96.

She added everything up, for a total of $3.66.

The form asked her to fill out the total amount in words. Mary did this. (Near bottom of form.)

The bookkeeper (Sandra Peale) approved the voucher (last line) and gave Mary back her $3.66.

1. The boss sends you on an errand downtown in your own car. You drive 12 miles. The company pays you 25¢ per mile. How much do you get for your car expenses?

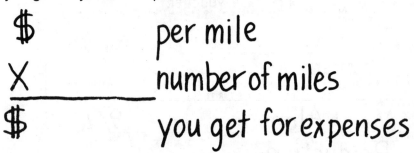

$ _____ per mile
× _____ number of miles
$ _____ you get for expenses

2. Your boss sends you out to pick up 4 photographs. The photographs cost $2.50 each. The bus fares cost you $2 total. You lay out your own money. How much does the company owe you?

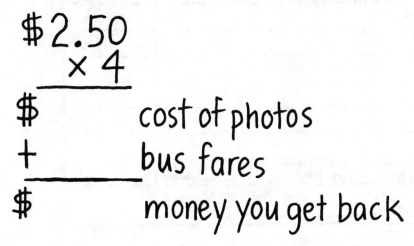

$2.50
× 4
$ _____ cost of photos
+ _____ bus fares
$ _____ money you get back

3. You are sent out to buy supplies for the coffee machine. You lay out your own money for: coffee—$4.60, paper towels—$.69, sugar—$1.59. How much are you owed? Show your arithmetic below.

4. You make a delivery for your boss in your own car. The round trip is 45 miles. The company pays $.20 per mile. How much money do you get back for expenses? Show your arithmetic below.

5. Your boss gives you $10 to pick up a copy of a report from a "quick-copy" place around the corner. The copy of the report costs $7.23. How much change do you bring back? Show your arithmetic below.

6. Your boss sends you to the Post Office to send a package express mail. The express mail package costs $9.95. While you're there, he asks you to buy $20.00 worth of stamps. Fill out the form below.

Be sure to fill in your name at the top. Fill in amount. Then add and show Total Amount. Then write it out in words (bottom left).

```
661-8/79
INSTRUCTIONS:              PETTY CASH VOUCHER
      1. USE THIS FORM TO OBTAIN REIMBURSEMENT FOR ANY AUTHORIZED PETTY CASH
         EXPENDITURES.

                        PRINT OR TYPEWRITE
PAYEE NAME:                                        DATE

DEPARTMENT TO BE CHARGED:              ACCOUNT NUMBER
                                  L    ACCT.    DEPT.    CODE

              EXPLANATION                          AMOUNT

TOTAL AMOUNT OF REIMBURSEMENT IN WORDS:    TOTAL  $
                              DOLLARS       AMOUNT
```

73

7. Your boss gives you $20 to make a delivery in the company truck. You spend $3.25 for tolls plus $11 on gas. How much do you give back? Show arithmetic below.

8. Your boss sends you on a trip to pick up a box of computer forms. She tells you to have lunch and the company will pay for it. She gives you $30. You spend: 2 train fares at $4.75 each
Taxi fares $6.80 total
Lunch $3.90

How much money do you bring back?

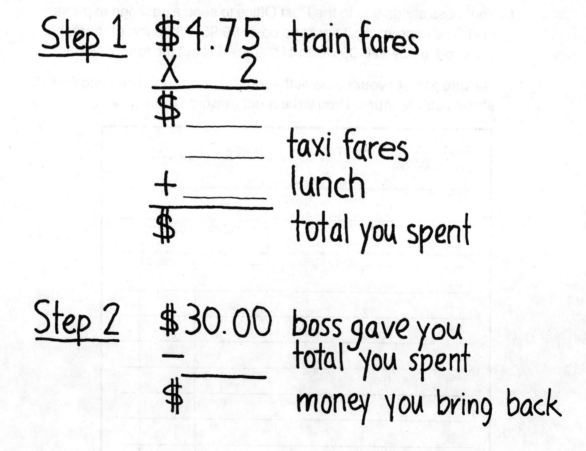

Step 1 $4.75 train fares
  X   2
$ _____

_____ taxi fares
+ _____ lunch
$ _____ total you spent

Step 2 $30.00 boss gave you
− _____ total you spent
$ _____ money you bring back

33 ▌▌▌▌▌▌▌▌▌▌▌▌▌▌▌▌▌▌▌▌▌▌▌▌▌▌
PAYING FOR THINGS BY CHECK

Mary Franklin has a bank checking account. She just brought a sweater for $21.73 (with sales tax). She paid for it by check.

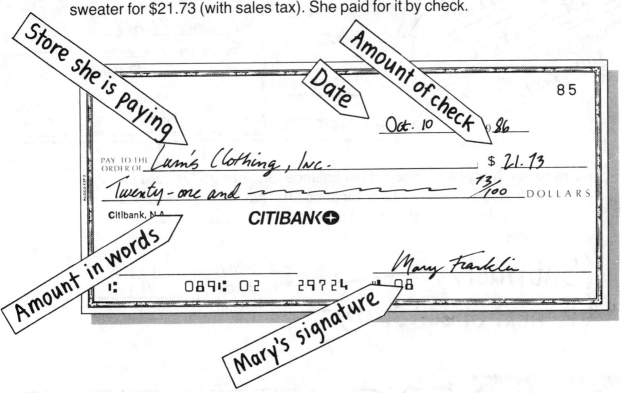

Notice how Mary writes the amount out in words.

She writes the "Twenty-one" (for dollars) followed by "and." Then she draws a long line.

At the end of the line she writes $\frac{73}{100}$ (for cents).

Mary keeps track of the purchase on the **check stub** that is left when she tears off the check. She also figures out her **balance**—the money she still has in the bank.

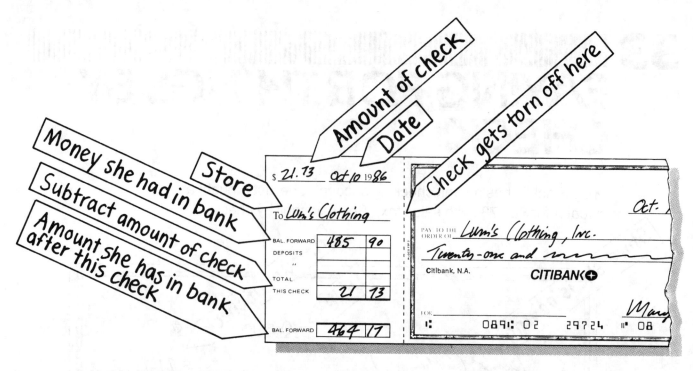

Notice how Mary keeps track of her balance. She **brings forward** the amount from the previous check (or deposit). That means she copies the amounts from her last check stub. Then she can subtract and get a new balance.

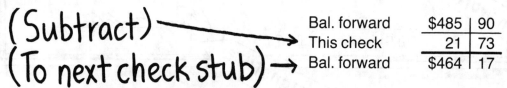

Bal. forward	$485	90
This check	21	73
Bal. forward	$464	17

Exercises

1. Mary next paid for a gift for her mom by check. The gift cost $16.15. She filled out everything except the amount in words. Write out the amount for her in the check. Be sure you write it this way:

Sixteen and 〰〰〰 $\frac{15}{100}$

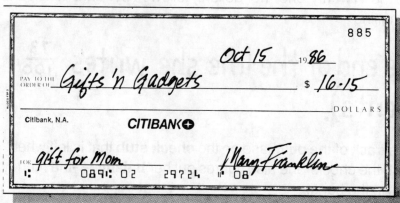

2. The check was for $16.15. Mary filled out most of the stub. She still has to subtract to get the new "Bal. forward." Do this for her.

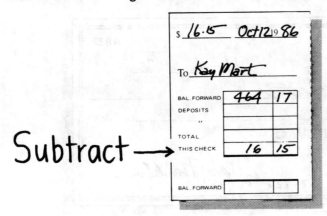

3. Mary paid her rent by check. The amount of the rent was $153.30. Fill in the amount in numbers **and** words.

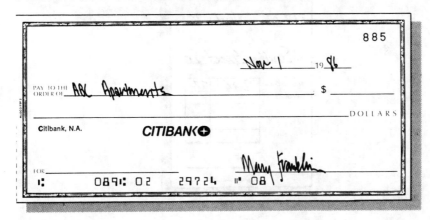

4. The rent was $153.30. Find Mary's new "Bal. forward" (on the stub).

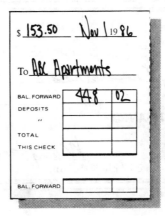

5. Mary paid her gas and electric bill by check. The amount was $18.02. Fill in the amounts:

6. Find her new "Bal. Forward" (after the gas and electric payment).

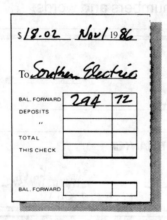

7. Mary treated her friend to supper. The bill came to $15.40. She paid by check. Fill in the amounts.

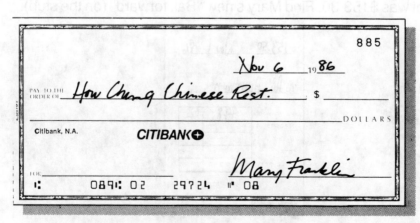

8. Find her new balance (after the check above).

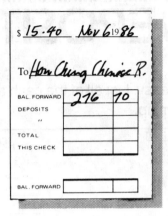

$15.40   Nov 6 19 86

To Hon Chung Chinese R.

BAL. FORWARD	216	70
DEPOSITS		
''		
TOTAL		
THIS CHECK		
BAL. FORWARD		

9. Mary bought a bus pass by check. It cost $19.50. Fill in the amounts.

Nov 10 19 86

885

PAY TO THE ORDER OF   Metro Bus Co. $ _____

_____ DOLLARS

Citibank, N.A.   CITIBANK⊕

FOR _____   Mary Franklin

⑆ 089⑈ 02   29724 ⑆ 08

10. Find Mary's new balance (after the bus pass check).

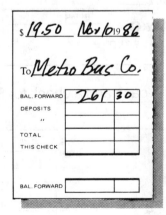

$19.50   Nov 10 19 86

To Metro Bus Co.

BAL. FORWARD	261	30
DEPOSITS		
''		
TOTAL		
THIS CHECK		
BAL. FORWARD		

34 BANK DEPOSITS

Making a bank deposit is easy. List all of the cash and checks you are depositing. Then add them up.

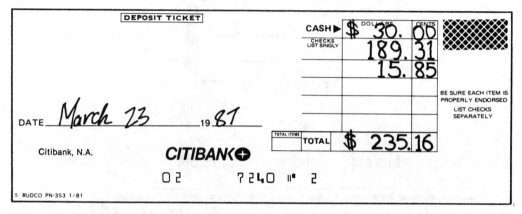

Elena deposited $30.00 in cash. She also deposited 2 checks. One was her paycheck for $189.31. The other was for $15.85. The total was $235.16.

Exercises

1. Elena deposits 3 checks. One is for $25.00. The second is for $49.95. The third is for $72.50. Write up the deposit.

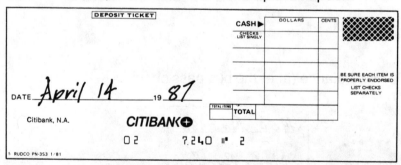

2. Elena deposits $45.25 in cash and a check for $105.47. Write up the deposit.

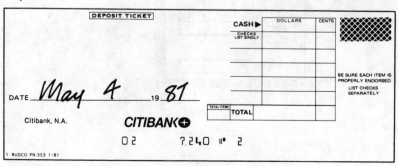

3. Elena deposits her paycheck for $189.31 and another check for $7.00. Write up the deposit.

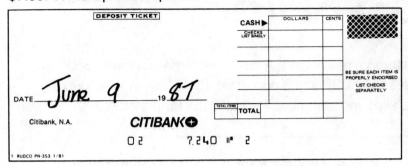

4. Elena deposits just one check for $189.31. List the check. Then bring it down for the Total.

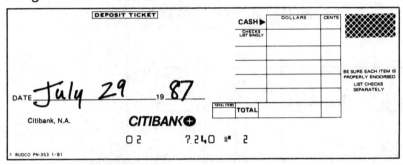

5. Elena's paycheck is $189.31. She wants to take $60.00 out in cash for herself. How much will she deposit? (Subtract.)

6. When she gets her next paycheck, Elena decides to take $70.00 out in cash. How much is left for deposit from the $189.31? List this amount under "Cash."

Then add in a check for $23.00 and complete the deposit slip.

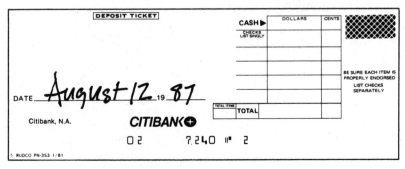

35 SALES SLIPS

Sam is a waiter in a restaurant. A customer orders a ham sandwich, ($2.25), a salad ($1.00), and a cup of tea ($.40). Sam writes up the check (sales slip), including the 7% sales tax for his area.

HARBOR RESTAURANT

DATE *June 15, 1986*

ham sandwich	$ 2	25
Salad	1	00
tea		40
SUBTOTAL	3	65
7% TAX		26
TOTAL	$ 3	91

To figure the sales tax, Sam had to multiply $3.65 (the **subtotal**) × .07. Or he could have used a tax table. Or he may have gotten to know the tax on various amounts in his head.

1. Sam wrote up the sales slip below. Figure out the sales tax. Then add it to the subtotal.

HARBOR RESTAURANT

DATE _June 15, 1986_

Ice Cream	$	75
Pie		95
Milk		50
SUBTOTAL	$ 2	20
7% TAX		
TOTAL		

$2.20
× .07 (7% tax)

_____ (Go to the next higher penny.)

2. Figure out Sam's tax on this sales slip. Then add it to the subtotal.

HARBOR RESTAURANT

DATE _June 15, 1986_

Hamburger	$ 1	50
Milk		50
SUBTOTAL	$ 2	00
7% TAX		
TOTAL		

3. Figure out the sales tax on this sale slip from a hardware store. (Tax is 5%.) Then add it to the subtotal.

ECONOMY HARDWARE		
DATE Jan 23, 1981		
GLUE	$	95
RULER		45
SUBTOTAL	$ 1	40
5% TAX		
TOTAL		

4. Figure out the sales tax on this sales slip from the hardware store. Then get your total. (Note that only one item was purchased.)

ECONOMY HARDWARE		
DATE Jan 23 1981		
1 gal. paint	$ 6	00
SUBTOTAL	$ 6	00
5% TAX		
TOTAL		

5. Add up this sales slip. Then figure sales tax and total.

ECONOMY HARDWARE

DATE _Jan 23, 1987_

	$	
washers	$	40
pipe wrench	8	00
caulk	2	90
SUBTOTAL		
5% TAX		
TOTAL		

6. Add up this sales slip. Then figure sales tax and total.

ECONOMY HARDWARE

DATE _Jan 23, 1987_

	$		
1½" nails	$	1	35
WD-40		2	75
2 light bulbs		1	40
SUBTOTAL			
5% TAX			
TOTAL			

7. Write up a sales slip for the following purchase at Economy Hardware: ¼″ staples $.95, Gold Enamel $1.75, 1 paint brush $1.50.

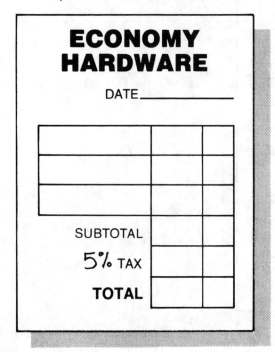

ECONOMY HARDWARE

DATE_____

SUBTOTAL		
5% TAX		
TOTAL		

8. Write up a sales slip for the following purchase: Econo screwdriver set $3.95, Hammer $5.99, Pliers—special price $1.95. When you figure the tax, go to the next higher penny.

ECONOMY HARDWARE

DATE_____

SUBTOTAL		
5% TAX		
TOTAL		

36 ||||||||||||||||||||||||||||||||||||||||||||
INVOICES

An invoice is like a sales slip, only a little more complicated.

Look at the Oxford Plastics Corp. invoice below. Fyne Wig Stores ordered 50 Styrofoam Heads. They cost $1.00 each. 50 × $1.00 = $50.00. Sales tax (6%) on $50.00 is $3.00. Shipping was $10.00. Total amount owed —$63.00

OXFORD PLASTICS CORP.
4 Sandy Blvd.
Tacoma, WA 98404

SOLD TO Fyne Wig Stores, Inc.
8 Garden Place
Seattle, WA 98104

INVOICE
No.   683

ITEM NO.	QUANTITY	DESCRIPTION	PRICE	AMOUNT
FP6-X09	50	Styrofoam Heads	1.00	50.00
			Sub Total	50.00
			Sales Tax	3.00
			Shipping	10.00
		RETURN INVOICE COPY WITH PAYMENT	TOTAL	63.00

Please Pay This Amount ⟶

Oxford Plastics sold 30 Styrofoam Heads to J&P Manufacturing.

1. Figure out the Amount.

2. Bring down your subtotal. Then figure your tax (6%).

3. Add $7.21 for Shipping to complete the invoice.

OXFORD PLASTICS CORP.
4 Sandy Blvd.
Tacoma, WA 98404

SOLD TO *J&P Manufacturing*
2441 N. Apple Ave
Wilmette, IL 50092

INVOICE
No. 34683

ITEM NO.	QUANTITY	DESCRIPTION	PRICE	AMOUNT
FP6-X09	*30*	*Styrofoam Heads*	*$1.00*	
			Sub Total	
			Sales Tax	
			Shipping	
		RETURN INVOICE COPY WITH PAYMENT	TOTAL	

Please Pay This Amount ⟶

88

Oxford Plastics sold 110 Plastic Wing Sets to Gray Toy Co. They cost $1.50 each.

4. Figure out the Amount.

5. Bring down your Subtotal. Then figure your Tax (6%).

6. Add $18.45 for Shipping to complete the invoice.

OXFORD PLASTICS CORP.
4 Sandy Blvd.
Tacoma, WA 98404

SOLD TO *Gray Toy Co.*
Lewiston Industrial Pk.
Lewiston, ME 04240

INVOICE

No. 468

ITEM NO.	QUANTITY	DESCRIPTION	PRICE	AMOUNT
WS9-001	110	Plastic Wing Sets	$1.50	
			Sub Total	
			Sales Tax	
			Shipping	
		RETURN INVOICE COPY WITH PAYMENT	TOTAL	

Please Pay This Amount ⟶

89

Oxford Plastics made a sale to Fisher & Jones Co. It sold 65 Styrofoam Heads at $1.00 each **plus** 32 Plastic Wing Sets at $1.50 each.

7. Write in the items and the Quantities.

8. Figure out the Amounts.

9. Add up your Subtotal.

10. Figure the Tax.

11. Add $19.10 for Shipping to complete the invoice.

OXFORD PLASTICS CORP.
4 Sandy Blvd.
Tacoma, WA 98404

SOLD TO *Fisher & Jones Co.*
1221 E. Meadow Parkway
Rochester, NY 14620

INVOICE
No. 346

ITEM NO.	QUANTITY	DESCRIPTION	PRICE	AMOUNT
FP6-X09				
WS9-001				
			Sub Total	
			Sales Tax	
			Shipping	
		RETURN INVOICE COPY WITH PAYMENT	TOTAL	

Please Pay This Amount ⟶

90

REVIEW

1. Your boss sends you on an errand in your own car. You drive 20 miles. The company pays 25¢ per mile. How much do you get for your car expenses?

$ _____ per mile

× _____ number of miles

$ _____ you get in expenses

2. Your boss sends you out to buy some supplies. The bus fare costs $.90 each way. The supplies cost $4.15. How much money do you get back?

$.90 bus fares
× 2

$ _____ total bus fares

+ _____ supplies

$ _____ money you get back

3. You make a delivery in the company car. You spend $8.00 for gas, $2.50 for tolls; and $3.95 for parking. How much money do you get back?

4. Your boss gives you $10.00 to pick up some file folders. The file folders cost $9.20. How much change do you bring back?

5. Your boss gives you $20.00 to make a delivery in your own car. You drive 40 miles. The company pays you $.20 per mile. You also pay $3.75 in tolls. How much money will you give back?

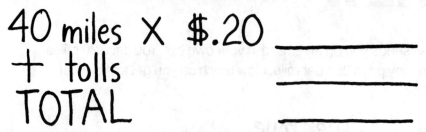

40 miles X $.20 _____

+ tolls ========

TOTAL _____

Subtract Total from the amount of money your boss gave you.

6. Josh pays his rent by check. It costs $169.50 per month. Fill in the amount on the check—in 2 places.

885

Aug 1 19 86

PAY TO THE ORDER OF Delano Management Co. $ _____

_____ DOLLARS

Citibank, N.A.

CITIBANK

FOR _____ Joshua Logan

089: 02 29724 08

7. Josh has $185.75 in the bank. He filled out most of the check stub. But he still has to figure the new Balance. Do it for him.

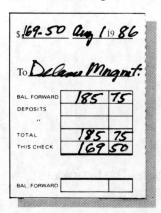

$169.50 Aug 1 19 86

To Delano Mngmt.

BAL. FORWARD	185	75
DEPOSITS		
"		
TOTAL	185	75
THIS CHECK	169	50
BAL. FORWARD		

8. Jed made a bank deposit so he could write some checks. The deposit was for $20.00 in cash plus a check for $35.00. Write up the deposit slip. Be sure to add to get the Total.

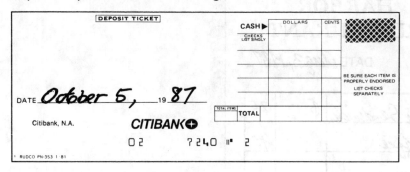

9. Jed has $51.25 in the bank. He paid his telephone bill for $20.10. Complete the check. Then complete the check stub.

10. Figure out the sales tax (5%) on this sales slip. Then add it to the Subtotal.

HARBOR RESTAURANT

DATE *Sept. 18, 1986*

Hamburg Plate	$3	95
Coke		45
SUBTOTAL	$4	40
5% TAX		
TOTAL		

11. Figure out the sales tax on this sales slip. Then add up the Total.

HARBOR RESTAURANT

DATE *Aug 3, 1987*

Fish Sandwich	$ 2	20
Coffee		40
SUBTOTAL	$ 2	60
5% TAX		
TOTAL		

12. Add to get your Subtotal on this sales slip. Then figure your sales tax and total.

HARBOR RESTAURANT

DATE *July 4, 1987*

Chicken Soup	$ 1	00
Apple cake	1	25
milk		55
SUBTOTAL		
5% TAX		
TOTAL		

ABC Toy Co. made a sale to The Kiddy Store in the Mall. It sold 12 "Happy" Dolls at $4.00 each and 6 groom sets at $1.50 each.

13. Figure out the amounts for each item. (12 × $4.00 and 6 × $1.50).

14. Bring down your Subtotal.

15. There is no sales tax in this case, but shipping was $5.95. Add this in and get your total.

ABC TOY COMPANY, INC.

222 NORTH BALBOA AVENUE
ENCINO, CA 91347

SOLD TO *The Kiddy Store*
Lamberton Town Mall
Lamberton, MO 62833

INVOICE
No. 34683

ITEM NO.	QUANTITY	DESCRIPTION	PRICE	AMOUNT
07792-C	12	'Happy' Dolls	$4.00	
02388-N	6	Groom Sets	1.50	
			Subtotal	
			Sales Tax	
			Shipping	
		RETURN INVOICE COPY WITH PAYMENT	TOTAL	

Please Pay This Amount ─────

After the Kiddy Store received the shipment, it made a sale to Mrs. Alonso. It sold 2 Happy Dolls at $7.95 each and one Groom Set at $2.95.

16. Figure out the amounts for each.

17. Bring down your subtotal.

18. Figure your sales tax (5%).

19. The shipping charge is $3.20. Add this in and get your total.

The Kiddy Store

Lamberton Town Mall
Lamberton, MO 62833

Date *Nov. 11, 1987*

No.	Item	Am't
2	Happy Dolls - $7.95 each	
1	Groom Set $2.95	
	SUBTOTAL	
	5% TAX	
	SHIPPING	
	TOTAL	